Severn Valley Railway Reco

The Story of 'The Flo

The evening of June 19th 2007. The gathering storm!

SEVERN VALLEY RAILWAY

FLOOD DAMAGE APPEAL

"Your Railway Needs You!"

www.svr.co.uk/appeal

Contents

Acknowledgments

© Phil Sowden, 2012
Photos: © Phil Sowden archive unless otherwise credited.
Characters © Ken Kimberley author of Oi Jimmy Knacker, Heavo Heavo Lash Up & Stow and Knock Down Ginger (Published by Silver Link)

First published in 2012
Silver Link Publishing Ltd
The Trundle
Ringstead Road
Great Addington
Kettering
Northants NN14 4BW

ISBN 978 1 85794 392 4

Tel/Fax: 01536 330588
email: sales@nostalgiacollection.com
Website: www.nostalgiacollection.com

British Library Cataloguing in Publication Data
A catalogue record for this book is available from the British Library.

Printed and bound in Ceská Republika

This book has been produced to document the damage inflicted on the Severn Valley Railway during 2007 by a weather event of the type that would seem to be becoming more frequent. The work involved and methods used in rebuilding the railway are also described. A vast amount of information and data was collected during the work – if it was all utilised it would stretch to several volumes. Similarly it has not been possible to include other issues such as procurement of funding, publicity, communications and, not least, the personal thoughts and feelings of those involved; perhaps at some future date they will also be written down.

While the initial damage could not have been predicted, the work to rebuild the line could not and indeed would not have happened without the support and help of a great many people, ranging from individuals to major organisations who gave time, equipment, labour and financial assistance. The SVR would not be operating today without that help, assistance and goodwill.

The illustrations included within this book were collected during the months that followed the initial damage. They were not taken with the intent of incorporating them in a book to document the work, but simply to record the events as they were observed. Thanks to all who have provided pictures to the SVR and permitted their use.

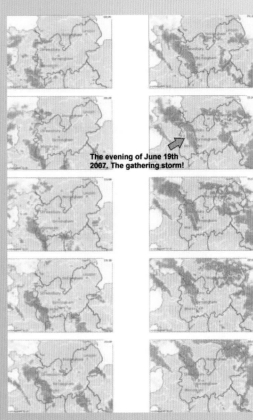

The evening of June 19th 2007. The gathering storm!

All weather maps courtesy of Weatheronline

HRH The Duke of Gloucester KG GCVO

KENSINGTON PALACE
LONDON W8 4PU

Rainfall, although often irritating, is usually considered benign. Global warming, we are told, causes us to need to expect more violent weather in the future and to prepare for storms and floods.

A heritage railway company is in many ways well placed to react to sudden damage. It represents a pool of historic knowledge, a deep well of engineering experience of all types and a fund of goodwill from the volunteers, who enjoy making their assets work to the greatest extent to inform and entertain the public of all ages.

This booklet shows how the damage that occurred as a result of storms in June 2007, was promptly and expertly repaired, enabling the historic trains once more to run, earning new friends and respect for the Severn Valley Railway.

Since the floods many people have asked if and when a book would be published to document what happened during those traumatic nine months in 2007 and 2008. I hope this book will go some way towards answering that.

The Severn Valley Railway was constructed during the 1850s to link Hartlebury, near Droitwich on the Birmingham to Worcester line, with Shrewsbury. In common with many secondary and rural routes it had declined by the early 1960s, and the line between Shrewsbury and Highley was closed to all trains in 1963. The southern end of the line between Highley and Bewdley remained open to coal trains until 1970, but eventual closure to all trains occurred in that year.

In 1965 the Severn Valley Railway Society was formed with a view to preserving the section of line between Bridgnorth and Hampton Loade for steam train operation. During the subsequent years the SVR expanded and by 1984 the line between Bridgnorth and Kidderminster was one of the major steam railway attractions in the country.

The SVR had, during its development from the embryo preservation scheme of 1965, been faced with a number of major challenges, but the events that unfolded during the evening of 19 June 2007 probably came nearer to closing the railway than any other previous event.

It had been a gloriously hot summer day, but during the evening the weather conspired to produce a major storm that travelled along the valley of the River Severn and caused major damage to the railway between Bewdley and Bridgnorth. During that evening the valley received within the space of a few minutes the equivalent of several days of rain; all drainage systems were overwhelmed, houses were flooded and road surfaces simply washed away. However, that was not the end. The following weeks saw further heavy rain, and by 20 July further significant damage had been caused to the railway.

The amount of rain that fell between May and 22 July was 348mm. The average rainfall for the equivalent period during the years between 1971 and 2000 was 153mm. Records going back to 1766 have indicated that the previous wettest period between May and July occurred in 1879, when 297mm of rainfall occurred.

The morning after the storm revealed many areas of damage and it was clear that the line was not fit for trains. However, following inspection the section of line between Bewdley and Kidderminster was found to be undamaged; in fact, the storm had skirted Kidderminster and comparatively little rain had fallen there.

While the line between Bridgnorth and Bewdley was not fit for use, the decision was taken to keep trains running on the undamaged section between Bewdley and Kidderminster. It was considered that this was essential not only to let people know that the railway was still in operation but also to generate some income while a scheme could be worked up and funding obtained to rebuild the damaged sections of line.

While the damage to the railway was substantial and everyone agreed that the task of rebuilding would be a significant challenge, at no time was closure or abandonment considered. The question was how much would it cost and how long would it take.

A number of people felt that the railway could simply 'fill in the holes' and start running trains again. However, such a simplistic approach would not offer

a viable solution. A properly considered engineering solution was the only correct way to resolve the problems and hopefully prevent them from recurring should such an event ever happen again.

This book shows some of the damage that occurred at various locations along the line and the methods used in reconstruction. Full engineering details of the various solutions adopted have not been given, but where it has been necessary to use engineering terminology efforts have been made to explain things in a simplified terms.

Given the extent of the damage that was found on the morning of 20 June and the events of the subsequent month, the fact that the line reopened to trains throughout its full length some nine months after the initial event can only be described as remarkable.

This book illustrates some of the damage that resulted from the initial storm and the following weeks of torrential rain. It also shows some of the methods and equipment used to rebuild the line and reopen it to passenger trains.

To describe the damaged areas in the sequence in which they were discovered, then to detail the repairs in strict chronological order, would be difficult, so the events are described in geographical sequence beginning at the north end of the line.

Above right: **A noticeboard relays the news.**

Right: **Donations poured in from members of the public, including the entire contents of this young enthusiast's piggy bank!**

OLDBURY VIADUCT

Oldbury Viaduct is located a short distance from Bridgnorth and is the first major structure that the railway crosses. The viaduct is brick-built and has five arches with a total span of 78 metres, the height from rail to the water course below being approximately 18 metres. When built the viaduct was designed to be of sufficient width to carry double track in order to accommodate a second track for the proposed but never constructed line between Wolverhampton and Bridgnorth. Situated just below the viaduct is Daniels Mill, a water-powered mill dating back to the middle of the 19th century. The volume of water flowing beneath the viaduct on the night of the storm caused serious damage to the water wheel and its associated

equipment, but fortunately no immediate damage was done to the viaduct itself. However, a washout adjacent to the Bridgnorth Outer Home signal did occur, which as can be seen undermined the trackbed. It also became apparent during the following weeks that the face of the valley between the viaduct and Daniels Mill was gradually sliding down towards the mill, putting the south end of the viaduct at risk of failure.

To determine the best solution a number of exploratory bores were made to establish the underlying ground conditions. Once the results from these boreholes had been received and analysed it was possible to determine the best engineering solution.

Left: **The bank between Oldbury Viaduct and Daniels Mill slipping towards the Mill.**

Below left **The boring rig being moved into position in readiness for pile-boring.**

The solution chosen was to install a contiguous bored-pile retaining wall alongside the railway immediately to the south of the viaduct. The first requirement was for the removal of the majority of track across the viaduct to enable the necessary heavy plant to be brought into position. The piled wall that was constructed comprised 25 piles each 450mm in diameter, with lengths varying between 7.5 and 10 metres, all linked together by a reinforced concrete capping beam.

In addition to the piled wall and capping beam, new drainage was provided. This consisted of vertical linked chambers either side of the track, which collected water from the uphill side of the viaduct via perforated pipes. Any water collected was then piped to the valley bottom.

Right: **The piles in place and the capping beam being constructed.**

Below: **The capping beam nearing completion and the drainage chambers under construction.**

Right: **The completed work at Oldbury Viaduct. The new drainage chambers and capping beam are clearly visible.**

The illustrations on this page show one part of the damaged embankment and some of the heavy plant being used to dig out and rebuild the formation.

Between Oldbury Viaduct and Knowlesands Tunnel three large sections of the railway embankment were washed out and deposited in the adjacent fields. Initially it was necessary to remove the railway track to give access for the heavy plant required for digging out any remaining unstable sections of the embankment. To rebuild these sections a technique known as 'reinforced earth' was used. In simple terms, this means removing any unstable sections of ground remaining and rebuilding with layers of fill material compacted and sandwiched between a geotextile mesh.

Left: **The embankment nearing completion. The top layer of geotextile material can be seen on the face of the embankment together with a section of the new drainage system installed beneath and alongside the embankment in this area.**

Below left: **The embankment after the application of topsoil and prior to seeding.**

Once the embankment reached its finished height and grade, the last task was to add a final layer of topsoil, which was then seeded with a general grass and wildflower mix to encourage growth and bind the surface together. In addition to the work associated with embankment reconstruction the opportunity was taken to install a new drainage system alongside the track. This consists of a concrete segmental ditch between the railway and the neighbouring trading estate; which feeds into a new drainage chamber and is then piped beneath the railway. In turn this pipe feeds into a chamber on the river side of the railway that is designed to release water at a controlled rate towards the river.

At the Eardington Summit the railway runs in a shallow cutting. During the night of the storm one side of this cutting failed in two places, and sections of cutting fell onto the track; at one of these locations a section of the neighbouring field was also washed across the track.

The solution adopted here was to rebuild the smaller of the failure sites with a crib wall made out of redundant concrete sleepers, while the other site was reconstructed using reinforced earth techniques. At both sites drainage pipes were installed to gather and direct any storm water onto the track in a controlled way.

Above left: **The scene at the top of Eardington Summit with mud and silt nearly 1.5 metres deep lying across the track.**

Left: **The collapsed cutting wall and part of the field that had washed across the track.**

Above right: **Rebuilding the cutting wall using redundant concrete railway sleepers.**

The volume of debris washed onto the track at both of these locations caused serious contamination of the track ballast. This necessitated removal and cleaning of virtually all the ballast between Oldbury Viaduct and Eardington Summit. To assist in this work the North Yorkshire Moors Railway loaned the SVR an item of plant known as a Track Gopher, which scrapes out ballast from beneath the track and transfers it to other rail-mounted vehicles to allow removal from the site for cleaning and reuse.

Above left: **A section of cutting wall rebuilt using the reinforced earth technique. Note how the ballast is badly contaminated with sand and debris from the field.**

Left: **The Track Gopher in use removing contaminated ballast for cleaning.**

Above: **The line to Eardington Summit following completion of the repair works.**

STERNS

The section of line that is known as Sterns has been a cause for concern since the railway was originally constructed. The River Severn at this location approaches the railway at almost 90 degrees before turning south towards Bewdley. Above the railway, which is carried on a low embankment above the river, the ground rises for some distance towards the village of Chelmarsh. The valley of the River Severn was largely formed during the last Ice Age and at that time the river valley was scoured out by glacial action. One of the results of this action was the depositing of bands of differing materials at varying depths, which could form what are known as slip planes. Such phenomena are present along most of the

to the north in the vicinity of Sterns Cottage.

Once the track had been removed, initial ground investigation work was carried out to determine the underlying ground conditions and, as anticipated, slip planes were confirmed. To overcome these and stabilise the railway a 45-metre-long contiguous bored pile retaining wall was constructed, which was in turn retained in place by 'soil-nailing' into the hillside above.

river valley, but in certain locations they have resulted in particular areas of instability. One such area is Jackfield, near Ironbridge to the north of Bridgnorth, and another is Sterns. On several occasions since 1970 it has been necessary to carry out work in the area of Sterns and in 1995 major work was carried out in an attempt to stabilise the ground. The work carried out involved tipping 3,000 tons of stone along the river bank to protect the toe of the embankment from erosion and also to toe-load the base of the slip plane. In addition to work on the riverside, a large ditch was also dug alongside the railway on the uphill side.

On the night of the storm and during the following weeks of rain this work prevented movement of the railway in the area of traditional concern. Indeed, the storm had a negligible effect on Sterns. However, the subsequent weeks of wet weather began to have an effect on the trackbed, not at the traditional site but just

Soil-nailing relies on steel rods being driven or bored into the hillside behind the area of concern until they are securely bedded into the surrounding solid ground. They are then if necessary further secured in place by the injection of grout. Once they are in place a 'pull test' is carried out on a representative sample to ensure that the process has been successful and they are securely in place. At Sterns the soil nails, where they protrude from the ground, are tied into and form an integral part of the vertical piled wall.

Right: **Water crosses the track near Sterns Cottage as a result of failed and blocked culverts.**

Above: **Work under way to stabilise the formation by means of soil-nailing.**

In total 75 vertical piles each 450mm in diameter and 7.5 metres in depth were installed, together with 37 soil nails 13 metres long and each inclined at 30 degrees to the horizontal.

To provide improved drainage in this area a new culvert was dug beneath the track just to the north of Sterns Cottage and a series of rubble drains was also provided to direct water into this new culvert.

Above left: **A 'pull test' being carried out on one of the soil nails.**

Left: **The vertical piles and inclined soil nails in place ready for the formation of the capping beam to tie them all together.**

Above: **The track back in place and awaiting tamping and final alignment. The concrete capping beam can be seen between the track and Sterns Cottage.**

FLOOD FACTS

To complete the repair we used –

- 4 kilometres (2.49 miles) of twin walled pipe – the distance from Highley to Arley.

- 7,000 sq metres (8,372 sq yards) of geotextile – equivalent to 1½ football pitches.

- 7½ kilometres (4.66 miles) of soil nails – the distance from Bewdley to Highley.

- 7,700 tonnes of material were taken off site, to designated landfill sites.

- 31,000 tonnes of stone were imported.

These last two items alone accounted for 2,500 lorry movements!

STERNS

Left: **An aerial picture of Sterns. The River Severn can just be seen on the left of the picture and the area of Sterns that has always caused concern is at the top of the picture. The new piled and soil-nailed retaining wall is clearly visible between the railway and Sterns Cottage, as is the new culvert, which can be seen crossing the driveway to the Cottage. Note also the area of ground immediately to the left of the cottage where a significant part of the drive has slumped towards the river.**

WASHOUT AT HAMPTON LOADE

started on rebuilding the embankment several days later but it was abandoned due to the prolonged heavy rain during the following weeks. The heavy rain also resulted in a number of the domestic septic tanks, installed to service the adjacent chalets, overflowing and depositing the contents on the ground surface.

The solution adopted at Hampton Loade was to remove the remainder of the failed embankment and rebuild using reinforced earth. New drainage systems were installed on either side of the track, leading to a drain across the neighbouring fields to the River Severn.

Left: **The collapsed embankment near Hampton Loade.**

Above right: **More damaged embankment near Hampton Loade.**

Right: **Repairs near Hampton Loade washed out due to the torrential rain.**

Just to the north of Hampton Loade the side of the railway embankment collapsed during the storm of 19 June. A significant amount of debris washed down towards the caravan park at the bottom of the embankment, but fortunately a fence around the site boundary prevented it from reaching the caravans. Work

Left: **The old embankment being removed prior to rebuilding.**

Below left: **The reconstruction of the embankment.**

Right: **The embankment approaching completion.**

Below right: **An aerial picture showing the rebuilt embankment.**

The failed embankment at Hampton Loade did not have readily available road access for bringing in plant and equipment of the size required to carry out the repair. This resulted in having to bring in all necessary equipment and materials via Waterworks Crossing, some 400 metres to the north. The provision of a drain leading to the River Severn also required permission from the adjacent landowner to cross the property, together with permission from the Environment Agency to create a new outfall on the river bank and also to discharge into the river.

HIGHLEY

At some time between 9.30pm and 10.15pm on the night of the storm a large portion of the railway embankment immediately to the south of Highley station was washed out. It was apparent that significant energy must have been involved in the destruction that ensued, especially where the chalets beneath the railway embankment were either destroyed or physically moved. Substantial volumes of water were still flowing out of the remains of the railway embankment down towards the river at 9 o'clock the following morning. It was also possible to see and hear further minor landslips occurring around the periphery of the main slip.

At Highley the slope between the river and the railway is of a two-tiered bench form. The lower section comprises the natural fall of the hillside, while the upper section is the railway embankment constructed upon side-long ground. The failure was caused by a washout of the upper railway embankment tier, which then flowed down over the lower tier. During the original construction of the railway the roadway that led from the main road through Highley village was diverted to enable it to pass beneath the railway. It appears that on the night of the storm major volumes of water came down this roadway, but rather than follow the road alignment to pass beneath the railway they simply took a straight line down to the river. Unfortunately the railway embankment was in the direct line and was overwhelmed within minutes. The failure mechanism and subsequent damage was akin to the overtopping of an earth embankment dam.

The washout of the embankment left the main running line unsupported and signalling equipment hanging in mid-air. The Highley Up Starting signal had also been washed away from its original location and was lying several metres away on what was left of the embankment.

Initially it was essential to prevent access to the immediate area while the possibility of further collapses existed. This entailed the evacuation of a number of residents from their chalets beneath the railway embankment and cordoning off the risk area.

As with the other damaged areas it was essential to understand in detail the failure mechanism that had led to the washout. After a number of days the railway was advised that the immediate danger had passed and preliminary investigation work could begin. The initial task was to retrieve the damaged railway equipment such as track and signalling, but this had to be done with extreme care. Clearly we could not bring in heavy lifting equipment as the track had been left unsupported and was unsafe. This resulted in most items being dragged back using cables attached to plant located in safe areas.

The initial clearance and salvage work had barely been completed when the next prolonged period of heavy rain occurred. On 20 July huge volumes of surface water were again flowing down the road towards Highley station car park. As this water crossed the car park and onto the cattle dock it was forming a fast flowing waterfall-type feature, which then temporarily pooled on the top of the railway. The ground upon which the embankment is constructed has a reasonably high clay content, preventing the water from soaking any further. The path of least resistance for the water was then through the embankment and out of the front face.

Above: **The initial view of Highley on the morning of 19 June.**

Left: **An aerial photograph of Highley station taken a few days after the storm of 19 June. The road leading down from Highley village to the station is just off the bottom of the picture, and the River Severn can be seen at the top. The extent of the initial washout can be clearly seen.**

Right: **Highley's Up Starting signal lies on the remains of the embankment.**

Below right: **Signalling equipment and track suspended in mid-air.**

Ground investigation work was carried out by means of boreholes and trial pits to enable an engineering solution to be established. After a number of weeks a preferred solution was decided upon. The results of the investigation indicated that the failure was not deep-seated, although evidence of relic slip planes was discovered. Similar conclusions had been drawn following initial ground investigation work carried out several years earlier on the site of the Engine House just south of Highley.

A number of possible solutions to the Highley washout were considered, but it was concluded that the most realistic solution would be to reconstruct the railway embankment with a combination of under-drainage and reinforced earth. The drainage proposed was a series of counterfort drains running at 90 degrees to the railway at approximately 2.5-metre spacing and up to 3.5 metres deep for the length of the washed-out embankment – some 100 metres overall. The counterfort drains would be stone-filled and linked together at the base of the railway embankment by a longitudinal drain that in turn fed via a new outfall into the River Severn.

A further complication associated with the work at Highley was that the material from which a large part of the damaged embankment was made was ash and cinder. This was not suitable for use in the rebuilding of the embankment, being classed as contaminated and unsuitable for reinforced earth construction. The consequence of this was that all excavated material had to be taken off-site for disposal at authorised locations, and any materials required for the rebuilding had to be brought in. The roads around Highley are not ideal for the movement of such large quantities of materials, and authorised routes had to be agreed before any material movements could begin.

Having established a solution, it was clear that the working area required would be significantly larger than the immediate washout area. It became necessary to remove the station water column and take down the cattle dock before any remedial work could start.

Above: **The view from the trackbed looking towards the River Severn.**

Above right: **The view towards Bewdley, showing the undermined track and signalling equipment.**

Right: **The view from the bottom of the railway embankment. The unsupported track is clearly visible together with the water tank and cattle dock, which had to be taken down before work could begin. Note also the vegetation that was flattened by the force of the water flowing across and through the embankment.**

Below: **Work under way on the drainage system.**

Right: **Construction of the counterfort drains beneath.**

The work at Highley was a major undertaking and certain safeguards had to taken to ensure that the ground remained in a safe condition as the work progressed. It was only feasible to dig and fill the new drainage system in sequence to prevent further weakening of the formation; similarly, if further significant rain had fallen it would have been necessary to immediately fill any partially completed drainage channels to avoid water entering and substantially weakening the surrounding ground.

Left: **Filling one of the counterfort drains with stone.**

Below left: **Rebuilding the embankment using reinforced earth.**

Below: **The view from the bottom of the embankment. The new access chambers that link the cross drains can be seen.**

Gradually the embankment at Highley began to take shape, and by November it was approaching completion. In common with the other sites rebuilt using similar methods, the finished embankment was topsoiled and seeded with a combined grass and wild flower mix to bind the surface together. The bottom ballast was laid by the civil contractor, then the SVR could begin track replacement.

Left: **The embankment rebuilt and with bottom ballast in place ready for tracklaying.**

Below left: **The SVR permanent way department steam crane lifts the first track panel back into place.**

Below: **A single line of track is back across the site of the washout.**

The trackwork at Highley in the area of the washout comprised a number of sidings and loops in addition to the main running line. It was decided that the first priority would be to re-establish a single line across the embankment, then the remaining track would be installed as and when time permitted. This policy was adopted simply to provide rail access to further damage sites south of Highley as soon as possible, and to ease the movement of materials to these areas.

Once work was complete on the embankment, the civil contractor began work on rebuilding the cattle dock and water tank, after which work concentrated on the new level crossing and revised road alignment necessary to give access to the Engine House.

TWIXT HIGHLEY AND BORLE VIADUCT

Opposite main picture: **Replacing Highley's up signal post during a misty November day.**

Inset left: **Works associated with the level crossing and road alignment near the Engine House.**

Inset right: **The main run-round loop and pointwork reinstated at the south end of Highley.**

Below left: **Walking the line south from Highley, the realisation of the size of the problem near Borle Viaduct becomes apparent.**

Right: **The problem!**

Below right: **An aerial photograph taken several days after the event showing the washout between Highley and Borle Viaduct.**

On the morning of 20 June no major problems had been reported between Highley and Arley, but that was about to change. At about 10.00am the Bewdley office received a phone call from one of our neighbouring farmers, who said, 'Do you know your embankment is in my field?'

Railway staff immediately set out to walk south from Highley to establish the extent of the problem. As the staff emerged from Stanley cutting the first signs of a problem were very much as shown in the adjacent photograph. The track had a very definite dip. As this came more into view it was clear that a significant length of track was totally unsupported and the embankment that should have supported the track was indeed lying in the neighbouring field.

Initially this site was of a lower priority than some of the others, but it was very quickly established that the method of repair would again be reinforced earth with additional drainage to a further river outfall.

Left: **A view taken on 20 July looking from the damaged embankment across the River Severn.**

Below: **Water off the fields cascades across the former embankment site.**

Before embankment reconstruction work could be started the rains returned and, as can be seen from the photographs, the area deteriorated further. The amount of water running off the fields and into the river was extraordinary. As can be seen, new watercourses were being formed across fields and the whole area was becoming overwhelmed.

Left **Work begins, literally dropping the damaged track.**

Above: **What was left of the embankment once the track had been dropped.**

Right: **The embankment has been cut away prior to beginning the rebuild. Note the abandoned sleepers at the base of the embankment.**

After several days the weather improved and work was able to begin at the site. One of the problems that had to be overcome was access for the equipment and materials necessary to carry out the repair. The solution was to access the site via a farm track some 300 metres north of the site; however, before this could be used it was necessary to widen it and clear the approach to the railway so that equipment could be turned and manoeuvred into place on the track.

Left: **The embankment approaches completion.**

Below left: **Replacement track is back in place across the washout site, awaiting top ballast followed by final alignment.**

The method of repair was to remove the remaining embankment, construct new drainage alongside the track, then pipe any resultant water across the fields to another new river outfall. While this work was under way the embankment was rebuilt as a reinforced earth structure. As at Highley the civil contractor took the formation up as far as bottom ballast in readiness for the railway to relay the track, but as the following pages show there was no rail access available from the south due to significant problems at Borle Viaduct, Victoria Bridge and Northwood, and the repair work at Highley was only partially complete.

Once the work at Highley was sufficiently advanced to permit the passage of engineering trains, work on relaying track could begin. New sleepers and rail were brought by rail from the north followed by final top ballast.

FLOOD FACTS

As work progressed it became very clear that the original estimate of £1 million was going to fall far short of the mark.

The final total came out at £3.7 million.

How the repair was funded –

• Initial grant from ERDF	£750,000
• Grant from AWM	£500,000
• Heritage Lottery Fund	£250,000
• SVR insurers	£850,000
(divided £500,000 for embankments and £350,000 for structures, signalling and track)	
• Further ERDF grant	£377,000
• Additional funds from insurers	£150,000
(specifically for work at Borle Viaduct)	
• Public appeal	£560,000
Total	£3,437,000

The remaining £263,000 was funded from SVR reserves.

FISH & CULVERTS...

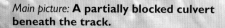

Main picture: **A partially blocked culvert beneath the track.**

Inset left: **Fish found at the side of the track between Hampton Loade and Highley.**

Insets bottom: **Blocked and damaged culverts at various locations along the line.**

Above: **Debris totally blocking a culvert entrance.**

Below: **The hastily assembled culvert cleaning and inspection train.**

Normally any storm water that falls along the valley flows downhill via recognised watercourses, then drains beneath the railway via culverts or, in the case of larger water courses, beneath bridges to the River Severn. The sudden intensity of the storm caused flash-flooding in many places along the valley, and one of the consequences of this was that a considerable amount of debris was carried towards the river. However, when the debris met the entrances to the culverts beneath the railway it very quickly built up and choked the culverts. In other locations the velocity of water passing through, together with debris being carried, caused damage to the culverts.

Prior to the storm the railway had plans identifying 28 culverts beneath the line. Following the storm a programme of detailed investigation of all railway embankments was instigated to establish if any 'unrecorded' culverts existed. By the time this survey had been completed the number of culverts beneath the line had increased to 108. The material of construction, the free area and precise location of all culverts is now recorded and identified by GPS coordinates.

One of the first tasks following the storm was to carry out a programme of cleaning debris away from culvert headwalls and approaches, and where necessary jetting and flushing was also carried out to ensure that any storm water could rapidly pass beneath the tracks. As part of this work all culverts were examined to confirm their structural integrity. Larger culverts were examined manually, while smaller ones were surveyed by remotely controlled cameras. In certain locations the extent of damage to culverts resulted in them being abandoned and new ones constructed alongside. These new culverts were constructed using various techniques including thrust boring and cut and cover. Finally, any culverts that were considered to be vulnerable to damage or disturbance by vandals were fitted with galvanised steel inspection covers and securely padlocked.

BORLE VIADUCT

Borle Viaduct, between Highley and Arley, is one of five major viaducts along the railway. However, due to its location it rarely appears in photographs. The viaduct has four arches and it is largely constructed of stone. During Great Western Railway days, additional 'jack arches' constructed of brick were added to prevent inward movement of the main piers. At some stage concrete training walls were also installed on the south-west corner of the viaduct to guide the water of Borle Brook beneath the viaduct. On the downstream side the existing stone walling remained in place. During 1976 the SVR had to carry out further major work on this structure to install a series of ten tie-bars transversely through the viaduct to prevent the growth of a longitudinal split that had developed; these tie-bars and capping plates can be seen towards the top of the structure. On the night of the storm the water level in Borle Brook, which feeds directly into the River Severn, just a short distance beyond the viaduct, rose dramatically.

When the viaduct was examined on the morning after the storm it was clear that a major amount of water had passed beneath it, and the vegetation surrounding it to at a height of some 2 metres above the tops of the jack arches had been flattened. The

Far left and above:
The downstream stone training wall is showing signs of failure.

Left: **The upstream concrete training walls are also showing signs of movement.**

velocity of the water had also succeeded in bodily moving the concrete and stone training walls on either side of the viaduct, causing them to fail. Both the concrete and stone training walls had kicked out laterally and large open cracks were visible between the concrete panels. As a result of this movement, the slope behind the training walls had become unstable. It was decided to secure the training walls in place by soil-nailing, with any remaining voids resulting from scour being filled with concrete, after which the whole area would be concrete-sprayed to form a continuous face. Work began on the upstream training walls during October 2007 and a total of 16 soil nails up to 27 metres in length

and inclined at 45 degrees were inserted through the remaining concrete walls, followed by concrete-spraying. However, the downstream stone training wall proved to be much more difficult to resolve.

Trial bores were made, but even at a depth of 30 metres nothing could be found that would provide a firm anchorage. An alternative solution was urgently required in this area as the stone wall was continuing to rotate and slide into the brook; this was allowing the embankment behind the wall to collapse, which in turn was relieving pressure on the viaduct itself and causing the stonework of the southern pier to separate.

Following further discussions with the Environment Agency a scheme utilising stone-filled gabion baskets at the base with a reinforced earth structure above was approved, and work began on this. Access to this corner of the viaduct was not easy, but this was overcome by bringing in long-reach machinery to lift materials across the brook to the work site. The separating stonework on the viaduct was anchored back together by a specialised contractor. However, the rains returned within hours of the long-reach machinery and other plant being moved into position to start work.

Left: **Nailing back the training walls on the upstream side.**
Below left: **The upstream training wall completed.**

Below: **Heavy plant at Fishermen's Crossing on the way to Borle Viaduct.**

Left: **Borle Brook in flood, preventing the start of work.**

Above: **The extent of the water – note that the lower jack arches are completely submerged.**

Below: **Work on replacing the stone wall and embankment is complete – compare the water levels with the picture above.**

Above: **An aerial view of Borle Viaduct following completion of the work.**

The accompanying pictures show the height to which the water level rose, and obviously all work had to be abandoned. By this stage in the repair of the railway the majority of the damaged sites had either been repaired or were sufficiently advanced for a reopening date for the line to be established. The one major outstanding problem was Borle Viaduct. If the water levels were to remain high and work could not resume, the proposed reopening would have to be put back. An estimate of the time to complete Borle was available, and by working back from the proposed reopening date a deadline for resuming work could be set, but it all depended on the water level in the brook going down sufficiently to allow work to restart.

Fortunately the water level did drop and work resumed with just a few days to spare. A coffer dam was constructed to allow placement of the gabion baskets to begin, and as soon as these were in place work on the reinforced earth structure began. Suffice to say that the civil engineering work was completed with just a few days to spare to permit relaying and track ballasting to take place.

VICTORIA BRIDGE

Upon approaching Victoria Bridge on foot from Arley it became clear that a significant amount of debris was lying across the top of the bridge, but the embankment was intact. However, on the far side of the bridge near the base of the Arley Down Distant signal there was what appeared to be a shadow on the ground. This turned out to be a major void in the trackbed immediately next to the southern bridge abutment. When the railway was built it cut through the ground to the south of the bridge in a fairly deep cutting, and as part of this work a stream that originally ran across this ground was diverted via a siphon to pass beneath the railway.

Above: **Having walked down from Arley, this was the first view of Victoria Bridge.**

Above right: **The hole in the track at the southern abutment of the bridge.**

Right: **Track suspended in mid-air at the southern abutment.**

The first message received about Victoria Bridge was that the bottom of the cutting had been washed away. The initial reaction to this was that somebody must have misunderstood, and they really meant that the embankment next to the bridge had been washed away. After all, how could you wash away the bottom of a cutting?

On the night of the storm this stream was rapidly overwhelmed and water simply cascaded down into the cutting. The resulting water surge flowed towards Victoria Bridge until it found the shortest route to the river, at which point it simply took the railway formation with it. The southern stone abutment of Victoria Bridge was partially uncovered as a result of the damage, but fortunately no damage to either the abutment or cast-iron structure of the bridge resulted. It is probably the first time since the 1860s, when the bridge was built, that the rear of the abutment has been exposed.

Following the initial storm the only damage areas between Bewdley and Arley were Victoria Bridge and Folly Point. A plan was drawn up to concentrate efforts on this section of line with a view to returning the Kidderminster to Arley part of the railway to normal operation as soon as practicable. This plan was subsequently overtaken by events at Northwood, as described later.

Initially the track at the south end of the bridge was removed to give access to plant and machinery. The only route to the site for such plant was along the trackbed from an occupation crossing just south of Trimpley Waterworks or from the fishermen's car park at the end of Northwood Lane.

Below: **Removing track across the void at Victoria Bridge.**

Right: **Heavy plant working near to the southern abutment of Victoria Bridge**.

The repair involved rebuilding a retaining wall at the bottom of the bridge once the public footpath had been cleared, after which the formation up to track level was reinstated using reinforced earth. Additional drainage was put in place on both sides of the track between the cutting and the bridge abutment, which fed into cross-linked chambers before feeding down to the river. The work at Victoria Bridge was difficult due to problems of access and lack of space to manoeuvre equipment and store materials. However, the bridge became the first of the major damage sites to be completed in terms of civil engineering work.

It was necessary to reinstate track across the work site at Victoria Bridge once the work to rebuild the trackbed was complete, so that materials could be brought in by rail from Arley for further work in Eyemore cutting to the south of the bridge.

It was also necessary to carry out some work on cleaning contaminated ballast on the bridge as well as removal of mud, silt and other debris that had washed part-way across the bridge. Fortunately the deck of the bridge had been changed from solid timber to open mesh a number of years previously, and this undoubtedly resulted in less damage and possible loss of some portions of the bridge decking.

Above: **Work under way at the southern end of Victoria Bridge.**

Below: **A new drainage chamber that feeds down to the river.**

Above: **New drainage systems feed into the chamber visible in the distance.**

Below: **Track is temporarily reinstated across the site of the damage.**

Above left: **Work under way laying the new track.**

Above: **Rails being welded.**

Left: **Trees across the track and water in the cess along the track near Trimpley.**

The track and ballast through Eyemore cutting immediately south of Victoria Bridge were covered in debris resulting from the stream above the railway bursting its banks during the storm. The rail in this cutting had been identified as a section due for renewal during the coming years, so the opportunity was taken to carry out a complete renewal of rails, sleepers and ballast.

Access to the cutting area was again a major problem. The line at Highley was still under repair and Northwood was only partially complete. Once the temporary track across Victoria Bridge was in place Arley was the nearest point to Eyemore cutting with suitable road access. However, rail is normally supplied in lengths of 60 feet, and the road access was unsuitable for such lengthy loads. The Severn Valley permanent way gang was fully committed at other locations along the line, and the railway did not have sufficient time to wait for them to become available, so the decision was taken to subcontract the track-relaying at Eyemore.

Following a competitive tendering procedure a suitable contractor was selected. The contractor brought in bottom ballast, sleepers, rail and all other materials via Arley station and transported them to the cutting. The rail was brought in as 30 foot lengths and, once laid, was welded together into 120-foot sections. Once complete the track remained without top ballast until a through rail connection from Eardington permanent way yard was available.

FOLLY POINT

Right: **Erosion by the River Severn at the base of the structure supporting the track.**

Below: **The gabion baskets supporting the track leaning 'the wrong way' at Folly Point.**

Far right: **Work begins on removing track and ballast.**

Below right: **New gabion baskets being installed.**

The railway at Folly Point is carried above the River Severn on a series of gabion baskets, which are in turn carried on a stone retaining wall. The

river at this point approaches the railway at almost 90 degrees before turning towards Bewdley. When the line was examined on 20 June the gabion baskets had been displaced, with their tops now leaning out towards the river. The hillside above Folly Point rises for a considerable distance beyond the railway and it appeared that this bank was pushing the railway towards the river. However, this was not the only problem.

The river bank was being eroded and the stability of the retaining wall was at risk. Urgent conversations with the appropriate authorities took place and within hours permission had been granted to tip stone into the river to prevent further erosion. Once this was done work on the gabion baskets and track formation could begin. The complete area was dug out and replacement baskets inserted together with new drainage to the river.

Above and below: **Installation of the new gabion baskets.**

Above: **The track back in place and ready for tamping.**
Below: **The new gabion wall and drain near Folly Point.**

Right: **All materials were brought to the site via the fishermen's car park at the end of Northwood Lane.**

In common with many of the damage sites, access to Folly Point was difficult, and all materials for the work had to be brought in via the fishermen's car park at the end of Northwood Lane. As work was progressing here it became apparent that parts of the hillside adjacent to the site were again moving and it was necessary to evacuate the site and suspend work while this was investigated and the ground stabilised. Specialist plant was brought in that was capable of 'climbing' the bank, which enabled a long rubble-filled drain to be cut into the hillside to collect and direct water to the drains below. A stone gabion wall was constructed just above the railway at this location to prevent any further debris falling onto the railway. Once this area was secured, the remaining work on Folly Point could be completed.

NORTHWOOD

Below: **Tension cracks alongside the track, discovered on 21 July.**

Right: **An aerial view of Northwood before repair work began. Northwood Lane and the chalets that had to be evacuated can be seen at the bottom of the picture.**

The railway between Bewdley and Trimpley is carried on an embankment that runs parallel to Northwood Lane. Only minor damage was caused to the railway in this area during the initial storm, but the rainfall that occurred on 20 July resulted in significant damage. The first indication of a problem was the appearance of tension cracks alongside the railway at the ballast shoulder. When these cracks were examined they extended vertically into the embankment for at least 2 metres – it was clear that the embankment was at risk of failure. Should this have occurred the embankment would have collapsed onto the roadway below and would probably have caused serious structural damage to a number of chalets located beneath it. Traffic on the road was diverted across the adjacent field and the roadway closed; in addition the residents of the chalets at risk were evacuated.

Above left: **A view from the top of the embankment showing soil-nailing in progress.**

Below left and above: **Views looking up at the embankment from Northwood Lane.**

A site investigation was begun to establish the best method of repair. It was found that in addition to the effects of rainfall significant amounts of water were being discharged in an uncontrolled manner into the ground by the chalets located above the line.

The solution to the problems at Northwood was again stabilisation by soil-nailing. Five rows of 91 soil nails installed at 25 degrees to the horizontal with a nominal 1.1-metre horizontal spacing were utilised. The design length of the nails ranged from 16 to 10 metres. In addition to the soil nails two layers of facing mesh were required to provide suitable bearing capacity for the head plates and to prevent localised failures between the nails. Once the soil nails had been installed and the embankment stabilised, the trackbed formation was dug out to a depth of 1.5 metres and reinforced with a geogrid material, after which this section was rebuilt, then the ballast and track were replaced. New drains were also provided to collect water on the uphill side of the track and carry it across the adjoining fields to the river.

Below: **A view looking north showing the soil nails in place with the facing mesh being positioned.**

Inset: **Relaying of the track begins.**

The area of soil-nailing was finally covered with topsoil and seeded to encourage regrowth of the ground cover. The soil-nailing work at Northwood took place between early November and late January 2008 and once again this period was very wet. As can be seen from the illustrations, Northwood Lane virtually vanished beneath the mud and work to re-establish the road surface was necessary once all other work was complete. The residents who were evacuated from the chalets beneath the embankment were eventually able to return to their properties during February 2008.

Below: **An aerial view of the Northwood embankment repair site. The heads of the soil nails are clearly visible.**

Right: **Thrust-boring a new culvert beneath the track near Highley.**

By 2010 vegetation had covered the area to the extent that the work site had become virtually indistinguishable from the surrounding area. Today trains cross the site, which took approximately half a million pounds to repair, in a matter of a seconds and most passengers are not aware of the work that had to take place to stabilise this 100 metres of embankment.

BRIDGE AT BRIDGNORTH

The northern end of the railway between Bridgnorth and Hampton Loade was by late January 2008 ready for reopening to passenger trains, and it was decided that the half-term holiday period beginning on Saturday 9 February would be the most suitable time. Appropriate arrangements were made and the press was advised. However, with just a few days to go the permanent way

Above: **The first train to travel from Bridgnorth to Bewdley following the repair work did so on 10 March 2008.**

foreman noticed that the track across the Cleobury Mortimer road bridge just outside Bridgnorth had gone out of alignment. An investigation was launched and it transpired that at some time during the preceding two days the bridge had been subjected to a 'hit and run' by a lorry, and the impact had displaced the southern end of the bridge by about 100mm such that it was no longer correctly seated on its bearings. An emergency road closure was authorised and the SVR steam crane was used to successfully lift the end of the bridge and relocate it correctly on the bearings. The lorry responsible for the incident has never been traced, but the northern end of the line reopened as planned.

On 10 March 2008 the first works train finally succeeded in running through from Bridgnorth to Bewdley. The train was hauled by electro-diesel No E6006 and as well as bringing through permanent way materials it also pulled locomotive No 47383 down in readiness for turning prior to its entry into the Engine House at Highley.

Left: **The SVR steam crane lifts the southern end of the bridge across the Cleobury Mortimer road back onto its bearings.**

Left: **A ballast train passes the site of the Engine House.**

Below left: **The locomotives are shunted into the Engine House.**

An official reopening of the line to passengers had been set for Friday 21 March 2008, just nine days after the first train had got through from Bridgnorth to Bewdley. It was also advised that a special reopening train would be running on 20 March for invited guests who had helped not only with the physical repair of the railway but had also provided funding and equipment utilised during the work. The days prior to the reopening were very hectic. Additional ballast had to be dropped at various locations along the line, debris had to be cleared, and the track required tamping through several large sections. The railway had also decided that the Engine House at Highley would also be fully opened on the same date that railway operations resumed, and all the rail-mounted exhibits still had to be positioned within the building.

The reopening train ran as planned on 20 March from Kidderminster to Bridgnorth, and on the return trip a stop was made during which all passengers were able to tour the Engine House. The train was hauled by locomotive No 7812 *Earlstoke Manor*, which had also only just been returned to use following a major overhaul. On the following day, 21 March, the railway was officially reopened for normal traffic. Was it by chance or was it planned that the reopening was exactly 9 months to the day following the discovery of the damage caused by the initial storm?

FLOOD FACTS (3)

Some lessons...

• Expect the unexpected

• The Engine House unlocked the funds to rebuild the railway

• The impact of the SVR on the local economy

• Make sure your insurance is adequate.

Additional points...

• Ensure that you put out one message that is clear

• Have one point of contact or spokesman

• Tell the truth – if you don't you will be caught out

• Keep people informed

• Use your marketing department

• Let your staff and volunteers know what is going on.

• Know your neighbours and keep them informed and with you.

Left: **KIDDERMINSTER** The reopening train is about to depart, hauled by the newly restored *Earlstoke Manor*.

Below: **HIGHLEY** Scenes within the Engine House.

THE ROYAL VISIT

Above: **HRH The Prince of Wales unveils a plaque at Kidderminster station commemorating the Royal visit.**

Within days of the reopening of the railway it was confirmed that a visit by Their Royal Highnesses The Prince of Wales and The Duchess of Cornwall would take place on 10 June 2008. However, this was not to be a simple visit as the Royal Train would be used to transport the party from Kidderminster to Bridgnorth, after which the train, complete with

Royal Party, would return by rail to London via Kidderminster. It was also made known that a request had been made for the train to be steam-hauled along the SVR. Locomotive No 6024 *King Edward I* was brought in specially to haul the train, with No 6201 *Princess Elizabeth* also being made available to act as standby should any unforeseen problems arise. The Royal visit was a resounding success, and HRH The Prince of Wales travelled on the locomotive footplate between Bewdley and Arley. The Royal party was accompanied in the train by a number of long-serving SVR volunteers and staff, and the visitors were also introduced to other invited guests at the various stations along the line.

Above: **Locomotive No 6024 *King Edward I* at Kidderminster ready to depart with the Royal Train.**

The Royal Train behind No 6024 climbs Eardington Bank near Bridgnorth on 10 June 2008. *Geoff Griffiths*